MISERY

BY
WILLIAM GOLDMAN

BASED ON THE NOVEL BY
STEPHEN KING

★

★

DRAMATISTS
PLAY SERVICE
INC.

2

The original Broadway production of MISERY was produced by Warner Bros. Theatre Ventures in association with Castle Rock Entertainment, Liz Glotzer, Mark Kaufman, Martin Shafer, and Raymond Wu, opening on November 15, 2015. It was directed by Will Frears, the scenic design was by David Korins, the costume design was by Ann Roth, the lighting design was by David Weiner, the sound design was by Darron L. West, the production stage manager was Jane Grey, and the stage manager was Chris DeCamillis. The cast was as follows:

ANNIE WILKES .... Laurie Metcalf
PAUL SHELDON .... Bruce Willis
BUSTER .... Leon Addison Brown

The world premiere of MISERY was produced at Bucks County Playhouse (Jed Bernstein, Producing Director), New Hope, Pennsylvania, opening on November 24, 2012. It was directed by Will Frears, the scenic design was by David Korins, the costume design was by Ann Roth, the lighting design was by David Weiner, and the sound design was by Darron L. West. The cast was as follows:

ANNIE WILKES .... Johanna Day
PAUL SHELDON .... Daniel Gerroll
BUSTER .... James DeMarse

CHARACTERS

ANNIE WILKES

PAUL SHELDON

BUSTER

MISERY

Prologue

A room in a house. There is one bed. A man lies there. He does not move. Might be dead.

From beyond the door to the room, the faint sounds of a television program like Chuck Woolery's "Love Connection."* Then, a kitchen timer is heard faintly from beyond the door.

The door cracks open, and Annie Wilkes appears in the doorway. She wears, as always, a cardigan sweater. Annie is like no one else on this or any planet.

She moves to the bed and begins to speak, with such tenderness.

ANNIE. Paul? It's me.

> *Paul makes no sound. Annie produces two pills from her sweater pocket, lifts Paul's head, opens his mouth, puts the pills in his mouth, and ensures they move down his throat. She lowers his head to the pillow.*

Nothing bad can happen to you now. Not with Annie here. I'm your number one fan.

> *Annie exits. The sound of the TV stops abruptly; Annie has turned it off for the night. In the silence, she reenters Paul's room, so close to him.*

(*Whispers.*) I'm your number one fan.

---

* See Note on Songs/Recordings at the back of this volume.

One

Now there is light—dawn. Sun floods in through the window. Annie is still in the chair, watching Paul. She sees him stirring and moves toward him.

PAUL. Where am I…?

ANNIE. Shh. You're outside Silver Creek. Colorado. This is my home.

> *Paul moans in pain.*

You're going to be okay. My name is Annie Wilkes. I'm a nurse.

PAUL. *(Alarmed.)* My legs… they're on fire.

ANNIE. Yes, I'm sure they are. Soon you can have your pain pills, your Novril, but it's not time yet.

PAUL. What happened?

ANNIE. You were in a car crash, Paul. When I saw your car at the bottom of that hill, I won't lie to you, I thought you were done for. I had to crowbar the door open and there was glass all inside everywhere, and you weren't moving. It was not easy getting you out… but I'm a determined woman and I did it. I laid you in the snow and forced air inside you and I said, "Breathe, you hear me! Breathe!" I had to make you live. And that's what I did. I got you up that hill and into my truck. You've had a couple close calls but that's all over now.

> *Paul shifts slightly and winces, reaches for his shoulder, which is in a sling.*

Your shoulder was pretty badly dislocated, too. That was stubborn but I finally popped it back in. But what I'm most proud of is the work I did on your legs. Considering what I had around the house, I don't think there's a doctor hereabouts could have done any better.

> *She moves the bedcover so he can see his legs. Paul looks down, is stunned with disbelief. But we don't see his legs yet.*

You have a compound fracture of the tibia in both legs and the fibula of the right leg is fractured too.

> *Paul inhales sharply.*

It's not nearly as bad as it looks, please believe that.

PAUL. Shouldn't I be in the hospital?

ANNIE. I'll get you to a hospital, as soon as the roads open. I tried calling but the phone lines are still down. But I could hear the bones moving when I worked on you, so it really is best for your legs to remain immobile for now.

Now she gently puts the sheet back over him.

PAUL. How long have I been here?

ANNIE. This is your fourth morning.

PAUL. And I was unconscious that whole time?

ANNIE. Almost all the time. But when I heard your first scream, I was so relieved.

PAUL. I was screaming?

ANNIE. Dying men rarely scream. They don't have the energy for it. I know.

Annie indicates a makeshift IV stand.

We don't need this anymore. That's some good news.

Paul looks at his arm, touches it, but it hurts to move.

PAUL. Will I be able to walk again?

ANNIE. Well, you won't go dancing for a while, but yes, you sure will. That's a promise.

Annie turns to go.

PAUL. Hey. Ma'am. In the car, next to me, there was a leather case…

ANNIE. I have it, Paul. It's safe.

PAUL. *(Very relieved.)* Thank God… thank you.

ANNIE. You're welcome. Now, no more questions. You need your rest. You almost died.

Paul takes this in.

You're in good hands, Paul. After all, I'm your number one…

PAUL. *(And now the memory of what he heard while unconscious makes sense.)* …my number one fan.

ANNIE. Your number one fan. Yes, I sure am. *(Smiles down at him.)* And trust me, there ain't no number two.

She exits, leaving the door ajar.

Two

Some time later. A timer is heard ringing, beyond the door.

PAUL. Ms. Wilkes. Ms. Wilkes!

    Annie enters.

ANNIE. *(Kindly.)* Well you don't have to scream your head off, you know I'm on the other side of the door.

PAUL. Could I please have my pills now? My legs, very painful…

ANNIE. Oh poor dear, it's like clockwork how your pain comes. I have your pills right here.

    She reaches into her pocket and takes out the pills. She holds them. Then sweet, almost shy:

Could I ask you a favor? I took the liberty of peeking inside your leather case. You don't mind, do you?

PAUL. Ms. Wilkes…

ANNIE. Please, call me Annie. All my friends do.

PAUL. Annie. Please.

ANNIE. Anyway, I see there's a manuscript in there.

    Beat.

PAUL. And you want to read it?

ANNIE. You don't mind, do you? You wouldn't mind if I read it? I wouldn't presume to do such a thing without your permission. I respect you too much.

    Paul pauses.

PAUL. Sorry, but I have a hard and fast rule about who can read my work at the early stage. Only my agent, my editor, and anyone who saves me from freezing to death in a car crash.

    Annie realizes this answer is yes. And it's a big moment for her.

ANNIE. Oh my, you'll never know what a rare treat you're giving me.

    Beat.

Heavens! Forgive me for prattling away and making you feel all oogy.

    She gives him the pills. He eagerly swallows them.

There you go. You'll feel better in a few minutes. I just can't believe that my hero is recovering in my very own home. The man who gave the world Misery Chastain. And here he is: Paul Sheldon himself!

He breathes a sigh of relief, and puts his head back on the pillow to rest. Annie exits to get the manuscript.

PAUL. *(To her offstage.)* I guess it was kind of a miracle... you finding me.

ANNIE. *(From off.)* Not a miracle at all—in a way, I was following you.

PAUL. Following me?

Annie reenters with the leather case.

ANNIE. Well, seeing as how I'm your number one fan and all, it wasn't any secret to me you were staying at the Silver Creek Lodge these past five weeks. You finish all your new books there, any good fan knows that. So some nights, I'd just tool on down there and look up at the light in your cabin. And I'd try to imagine what was going on in the room of the world's greatest writer.

PAUL. *(Can't help but smile.)* Say that last part again—I couldn't quite hear you.

ANNIE. *(Smiles back.)* The world's greatest writer. Well, the other afternoon I was on my way home from town, racing 'cause I'd heard that the storm was coming in hard, and there you were leaving the Lodge. And I wondered why in the world would a literary genius go for a drive when there was this monster storm coming?

PAUL. The literary genius didn't know there was a storm coming.

ANNIE. Lucky for you I did. *(Very sincere.)* Lucky for me too, because now you're alive and you can write more books. Because the world needs more Misery books.

Paul says nothing, but he is moved by her sincerity.

Oh Paul, I know all of the Misery novels by heart, and I swear that's true. All eight of them. I just treasure them so.

Annie opens the case with anticipation and looks at the title page. Her face falls.

PAUL. This one's not a Misery.

ANNIE. *(Deeply disappointed.)* Well, I gather as much because I don't see her name in the title. *Broken Places.*

PAUL. Last week that title was a metaphor. But yes, this is a different kind of book. It's not set in the 19th century, or the English countryside. It's not even a romance...

ANNIE. So what is it then?

PAUL. My agent would say it's an esoteric, pseudo-autobiographical character study that no one will want to read... But that's just her sense of humor.

ANNIE. I don't... Is that funny?

PAUL. *(Considering the question, then, wryly.)* Not really, no.

> *Beat.*

But since you asked... it's not like anything I've ever written before. It's about the world I live in, New York. It's about a man who had everything and then crashed and burned and lost his way.

ANNIE. Well, I can't help but wish it was about Misery. But you wrote it. And so I want to read it. I want to read every word you write.

PAUL. That means a lot to me.

ANNIE. Though... if I had your gift, if I could breathe life into Misery Chastain, that's all I would write. I'd want to write as much of her life as I could.

PAUL. That's all I've been doing for twenty years! Don't get me wrong, I'm not complaining.

ANNIE. It sounds like you are, just a little.

PAUL. Don't misunderstand me. Misery is responsible for all of my success, and I'm grateful for that. But there's another writer in me—a serious writer, of serious books.

ANNIE. Misery is serious. All eight of your Misery books are serious.

PAUL. Yes, of course they are. I just hope my readers will like it as much as they like Misery.

ANNIE. Well, I'm sure we will.

> *There is a nice beat between them.*

PAUL. Did you say there were eight Misery books?

ANNIE. Eight Misery books? Yes—*Misery, Misery's Quest, Misery's*

Trial, Misery's Lover, Misery's Gift, Misery's Challenge, Misery's Triumph, Misery's Dilemma. That's eight!

PAUL. Secret?

ANNIE. What?

PAUL. Nine.

ANNIE. Nine? Oh! Nine?? Why didn't you say?! When? WHEN? Please say "soon."

PAUL. Very soon.

ANNIE. *(So excited.)* Has it got a name? How stupid can I get? Of course it has a name. What is it, what is it?

PAUL. *Misery's Child.*

ANNIE. *Misery's CHILD*?! I'm going to have a heart attack! Oh Paul, I want to read it tonight.

PAUL. Maybe not quite that soon, but it'll be in bookstores any day.

> *Beat.*

How long do you think before the phone lines are back up? I'd like to let my agent know I'm still breathing. And my daughter… my daughter must be worried about me.

ANNIE. It's the pass, Paul—it's closed, so no repair trucks can get through. But if you give me their phone numbers, I can try them for you as soon as it's possible.

PAUL. Okay. Thank you. For everything. It's… well, ironic, to say the least.

ANNIE. What is?

PAUL. When I finished this book the morning of the storm I felt more alive and more free than I had in years. And then later that day, I almost died.

ANNIE. But I was there.

PAUL. Yes.

ANNIE. Oh Paul. We are going to be so happy here.

> *Paul isn't sure what to make of this, but this is a moment for Annie.*

I better get to feeding the animals, they don't like it when I am gone too long. *(Smiling.)* Just like someone else I know.

PAUL. Animals?

ANNIE. Just a half-dozen laying hens, the two cows, and Misery.

PAUL. Misery?

ANNIE. My pig. For a while I was so lonely here on the farm. Then I bought Misery and she's a real companion. Sometimes I have my morning coffee right in her sty, and she just chatters away. *(Sincere.)* I hope I didn't offend you by naming her after the brave and beautiful woman you made up. I told you I was your number one fan.

PAUL. I'm starting to believe you.

ANNIE. Do you know what she said when I told her Paul Sheldon was here? *(Imitating the pig—and brilliantly.)* Whoink!—Whoink! Whuh—Whuh—WHOINK!!!

> *And she is gone.*

PAUL. *(Shaking his head.)* Wow.

> *Lights fade.*

Three

> *The sounds of a utensil clinking against a bowl. Then light— noon, a couple days later. Annie sits on the bed, feeding Paul tomato soup.*

ANNIE. *(As she feeds him.)* Open wide. *(He does—)* Such a good boy.

> *She gets another spoonful of the soup ready—and suddenly she looks at him—almost shy.*

PAUL. What?

ANNIE. Nothing, it's nothing, nothing at all.

PAUL. Sure sounds like something to me.

ANNIE. It's ridiculous, who am I to offer a criticism to someone like you?

PAUL. You won't be the first, go ahead—

ANNIE. I know I'm only forty pages into the manuscript...

> *She feeds him—Paul swallows, gestures for her to go on.*

...and it is brilliantly written but then everything you ever write is brilliant—

PAUL. Pretty brutal so far.

> *She is hesitating to speak.*

Is it hard to follow? I know it jumps back and forth in time...

ANNIE. Well, yeah, that's hard, but it's not that...

PAUL. I know the language is complicated...

ANNIE. *(Interrupting, a burst.)* It's the swearing, Paul.

> *A beat.*

There. I said it.

PAUL. The profanity bothers you?

ANNIE. Every other word is the F-word. It has no nobility!

PAUL. Annie, this is real life, it's 1987, everybody talks like that.

> *Annie holds tight to the soup spoon, trying so hard not to spill.*

ANNIE. What do you think I do when I go to the feed store in town? What do you think I say? "Now give me a bag of that effing pig feed and some of that bitchly cow corn?" "Hell yes, ma'am, coming right the eff up?"

> *Paul is surprised at this, but also a little amused. Annie is doing her best not to spill the soup.*

And at the bank do you think I say, "Here's one effin' bastard of a check, now get off your effin' ass and cash the effin' thing!"

> *Annie stands and loses control of the bowl, and soup spills on to the floor.*

(Shouting.) Ah! There! There! See what you made me do?

PAUL. I'm sorry.

ANNIE. Sure you are!

> *The kitchen timer goes off.*

So I suppose you want your cockadoodie medicine. Well, you're going to have to wait until I clean this mess up.

> *Annie exits. Paul sits in silence, a little shaken, not sure what*

to make of what's just happened. Annie returns a moment later with a cloth and starts to clean up her spill.

Pause, as she cleans. Then—

My mother would have washed my mouth out with soap and water for using that kind of language.

Beat.

You don't need to use swear words in the Misery books, because they didn't use swear words at all back then. They weren't even invented in the 1860s. *That* was a better time. You ought to stick to the Misery stories, Paul. I say that sincerely, as someone who cares about you, as your number one fan.

She finishes cleaning.

You won't make me mad again, will you?

PAUL. No. I don't want you mad. I sort of depend on you, you know.

ANNIE. Yes, you do, don't you?

There is a beat. She hands him his pills. Then she fills his glass with soapy water from the bucket. She hands him the glass.

Paul looks at her in disbelief.

PAUL. Seriously? You swore, not me.

ANNIE. Take your medicine.

PAUL. Annie…

Beat.

After a moment, with hesitation, he puts the pills in his mouth, and takes a small sip of soapy water.

Annie, satisfied, exits.

Paul shudders.

Four

Afternoon. Paul is in bed. Now the door to the room cracks opens slightly and Annie's voice is heard.

ANNIE. Look who's come to stay with us.

And through the crack in the door, there it is: Misery's Child. *The hardcover book. Now here comes Annie, peeking out from behind it—She has never looked happier than she does right now. She hurries to Paul.*

They had it at the general store, Paul—a bunch of them—I just slammed my money down the second I saw it. *(So excited.)* Paul—I got the first copy! Is that great or is that great!

PAUL. I'll say—it means the roads are open.

ANNIE. Well, the one to town is, but that's about it for now. But I called the hospital and talked to the head honcho—I told him who you were and what had happened. He said as long as there's no infection, you're not in any danger, and as soon as the road to the hospital is open, they'll send an ambulance for you.

PAUL. So the phones are working again?

ANNIE. Well mine's still out, wouldn't you know. But the ones in town were just fine.

PAUL. Were you able to reach my agent? I gave you her number remember, Marcia Sindell?

ANNIE. What do you think I've been doing, Paul—I called her. I told her everything.

PAUL. I need to be back in New York for this press launch.

ANNIE. You could just hear the relief in her voice. I gave her my number and once things are ship-shape here, she'll call you.

PAUL. Did you reach my daughter?

ANNIE. Your agent said she'd call your daughter and tell her everything. *(Closing that conversation, and back to her excitement.)* Now I know that this new manuscript-book is so important to you, but I have to put it down now that I've got this. *(So moved now as she opens the book.)* Oh Paul, I looked at the first page, and just to read the name Misery Chastain again…

> *She is just in heaven.*

It's like a visit from my oldest and dearest friend.

> *She is genuinely moved. Beat. Then, almost shy.*

Could I ask you a favor? I'd love it if you would autograph my copy. I already have your autograph on a picture, but it would mean so much to me to get it in person.

> *She brings the book to him.*

I know you're right-handed, so don't worry if it's not so legible. I'll cherish it anyway. It should say: "To Annie Wilkes. Who by saving me, saved Misery."

> *He signs the book.*

Thank you. Oh, Paul, you can guess it took all my self-control not to start reading it right there in the store, but I can't wait anymore. What a poet you are.

PAUL. Annie, there's something you should know about *Misery's Child.*

ANNIE. What is it? Something that happens in the book? Is Ian going to propose? She's not going to marry Geoffrey, is she? There are so many things I want to ask you, so many things I want to know.

> *Beat.*

PAUL. Well…

ANNIE. Oh gosh, no, don't tell me! If you tell me, I won't get to experience it for myself.

> *She sweeps toward the door.*

Paul—be honest now—do you like Liberace?

PAUL. Why do you ask?

ANNIE. I always play his records when I'm reading a Misery.

PAUL. When he plays Radio City, who do you think is in the front row?

ANNIE. I love you, Paul.

> *She is deeply embarrassed to have said this.*

I love your mind. Your creativity. That's all I meant.

And with that, she is gone out the door.

Paul just stares after her, shaking his head.

*And now—the lights grow dark. In the darkness, Liberace playing the piano and singing. "I'll Be Seeing You" is the song at the moment.**

Five

The very dimly lit bedroom becomes visible. Annie comes in with Paul's breakfast and pills.

ANNIE. Good morning! I made you my specialty, Scrambled Eggs à la Wilkes. I got up to page 100 last night.

PAUL. I guess that means it's okay?

> *Paul starts eating the eggs. Suddenly Annie breaks into a wonderful smile.*

ANNIE. Oh Paul, I love it. It's as good as all the rest. Better! The best! I can't even think of the word. Would "great" be insulting?

PAUL. I can live with great.

ANNIE. I knew she would marry Ian and not Geoffrey. But is Ian sterile or is she barren? They want a baby so badly. And I believe Geoffrey and Ian will become friends again eventually. Do they? No don't tell! I want to find out for myself.

> *Annie exits.*

PAUL. *(Quietly.)* Annie, Misery is dead.

> *Annie returns.*

ANNIE. I've got it—I know what's greater than great. What's the ceiling that dago painted?

PAUL. The Sistine Chapel?

ANNIE. Yes! That and *Misery's Child* are the only two divine things in the whole world!

> *She exits.*

---

* See Note on Songs/Recordings at the back of this volume.

Six

And now Annie and Paul are back in his room. Annie stands alone, staring out at the early sunset. Her tone is different than we have yet heard from her—lost in very deep thought.

Paul lies in bed, his hands under the covers.

ANNIE. I was married, you know. Years ago. In Denver. That did not work out. That was very, very hard. I was a nurse at a big hospital, so I threw myself into work just to get through the days. I worked nights too. Night shifts can be slow at a hospital so I had a lot of time to read. That was when I first discovered Misery. She came right at the point I needed her most. And after her horrible childhood, her miserable stepfather, to keep fighting like she does, she's always been a fighter. The whole world can be against her, but she knows that there's a justice higher than that of man, that God rewards the good in us. She makes me know I'm not alone in the world.

Paul lies in bed, his hands under the covers.

(A realization.) Though I realize you had a little something to do with that too. *(Another realization.)* And you must be a good man, or you could never have created a wondrous, loving creature like Misery Chastain.

PAUL. I'm…

ANNIE. All done?

PAUL. Yeah, thanks.

ANNIE. No problem.

Paul brings his hand into view as she comes to the bed—he holds a bottle—he has been urinating into it. Annie takes it from him, and holds it during the following.

I might have saved you from the car, Paul, but for all these years, you've saved me.

PAUL. You may be giving the books too much credit, Annie. I bet you would have been all right no matter what.

ANNIE. I don't know. I don't think I'll get married again.

PAUL. Me neither.

ANNIE. No?

PAUL. I wasn't very good at it.

ANNIE. Why not?

PAUL. Oh, um… I can get pretty obsessed when I'm working… I wasn't great about looking up from the typewriter. And the more success I had… I just wasn't there for my wife. Or my daughter.

ANNIE. But you dedicated *Misery's Child*, "To my daughter, Chloe, with love."

PAUL. Yeah, well, she's not really talking to me right now. I hope to make it up to her when I get home.

> *Beat.*

ANNIE. Well. I hope you don't think I can stay here chatting all night, I have got to finish the book! I may not be out of my room for a while, I get so caught up. Here's a glass of water, and your next Novril, and here's a *Reader's Digest*, it's not from this year but they don't go bad… I can't wait to get to the end!

PAUL. Don't you want to make it last?

ANNIE. Don't worry about that, the minute I finish I'll just start it over again.

PAUL. Annie…

ANNIE. What is it?

PAUL. It may not be what you expect, the ending. It was mostly unexpected to me.

ANNIE. But you wrote it, silly.

PAUL. I really hope you like it.

> *Annie moves to the door, turns.*

ANNIE. Of course I'm going to like it, I've never been more excited! Misery's about to have her child. What's it going to be, a boy or a girl—? *(Interrupts herself.)* —No don't tell me.

> *Now she puts her hand to her mouth—and throws him a kiss.*

Mwah!

> *Paul reaches out, makes a smile, catches it.*

19

She leaves. Paul looks at his hand that has caught the kiss, looks after Annie. He swallows the Novril, and sits for a while, as rain starts to fall outside.

Seven

Paul's room is dark. Outside a storm has begun. Growing. Paul lies in bed.

Suddenly, the door to the room flies open. Annie looks different now than she ever has. And boy, is she ever not smiling.

ANNIE. You dirty bird! SHE CANNOT BE DEAD! MISERY CHASTAIN CANNOT BE DEAD!

PAUL. Annie—please listen to me—

ANNIE. HOW COULD YOU KILL HER?!

PAUL. In 1871 women died in childbirth all the time—but her spirit is the important thing, and Misery's spirit is still alive—

ANNIE. I DON'T WANT HER SPIRIT! I WANT HER—AND YOU MURDERED HER!!

PAUL. I didn't murder her—

ANNIE. —THEN WHO DID?

PAUL. No one… she just died… she slipped away, that's all…

ANNIE. SLIPPED AWAY?! SHE DIDN'T JUST SLIP AWAY! YOU KILLED HER! Do you think I was born yesterday? A writer is God to the people in a story, he made them up just like God made us up. As far as Misery goes, God just happens to have a couple of broken legs and be in *my* house, eating *my* food, SO DON'T TELL ME YOU DIDN'T KILL HER BECAUSE YOU DID IT! YOU DID IT! YOU MURDERED MY MISERY!!!

She nearly hits him but manages to stop herself.

I thought you were good, Paul, but you're not good, you're just another dirty birdie—

PAUL. Annie…

ANNIE. I think I better go now. I don't think I better be around you for a while. I don't think it's—wise.

PAUL. Go? Where?

Annie moves to the door.

Will you be back to give me my medication?

ANNIE. Oh I think you've caused enough suffering and now it's your turn to suffer. And don't even think about anybody coming for you, not the doctors, not your agent, not your daughter, because I never called them. Nobody knows you're here. And you better hope nothing happens to me because if I don't come back, you die.

And on that, she's gone. For the first time, the door slams all the way shut.

Paul is alone.

Deafening thunder.

And now another growling sound—a car motor.

Growling, then gone. Paul takes a breath—

—stares across at the closed door—

—makes a decision.

Deep breath now.

Now another.

And here he goes.

Slowly getting out of bed.

He reaches down with his left arm, the good one—the right shoulder is the bandaged one, the shoulder that was dislocated—reaches to the floor—

—planning to gradually bring himself down.

Good plan—

—not such good execution.

His body twists as he falls—

—falls hard—

—landing dead on his dislocated shoulder.

Paul cannot help his shriek of pain.

He lies there for a moment, trying not to pass out.

And for the first time now, we can see his legs.

Nightmare time.

From the knees up, his legs are swollen and throbbing and horribly bruised and discolored.

But from the knees up, that's the good part.

From the knees down, he resembles an Egyptian mummy.

Annie's splinted his lower legs with slim steel rods that look like the hacksawed remains of aluminum crutches—

—and there is taping all around.

Now, more thunder.

And Paul begins so slowly to move.

Crawling, crawling—

—toward the door.

Each time he moves his legs, it's awful.

And each time the pain grows worse and worse.

He is closer and closer to total collapse.

But he hangs tough.

Outside, a terrible winter storm.

Inside, not a lot better.

The pain keeps growing.

But he won't goddamnit quit.

He's halfway to the door now.

Going slower and slower.

Now three quarters of the way.

Much slower.

Hardly able to move at all.

Keeps on.

And on.

At last he's there—

Reaches up.

Grabs the doorknob.

Turns the damn thing.

Locked.

PAUL. Motherfucker.

His arm falls.

His eyes close.

Outside, the storm only grows.

Inside… no movement. A man lies there.

Could be dead.

Eight

Daylight. A gray day. Paul lies helpless on the floor. Could be the worst shape we've seen him in. Annie unlocks the door, starts inside, stops suddenly as she sees Paul. She is stunned.

ANNIE. Oh my God—Oh my God—

She kneels alongside him.

Have you been on the floor all this time? This is all my fault—leaving you alone.

Paul tries to speak, can't. Finally, he manages a nod.

I have to get you into the bed.

PAUL. Oh please. Wait… Wait!

She begins to drag him toward the bed.

Ah, pain…! Annie, for God's sake.

And now she puts her strong arms under his body. She hoists him onto the bed. It is excruciating for Paul.

ANNIE. Are you okay?

PAUL. *(In agony.)* Perfect.

23

Smiles sweetly at him now.

ANNIE. I have the biggest surprise of your life coming up—but first, there is one thing you must do.

PAUL. *(Through great pain.)* How about my pills and a little snack while I wait for my surprise.

ANNIE. I'll get them for you, but first you must listen to me. Now I know that sometimes my thinking is a little muddy. I can't always tell what's right. I accept that. But this time I thought so clearly—because I asked God about you. *(Carefully choosing her words.)* And God said, "I delivered Paul Sheldon unto you so that you could shew him the way."

PAUL. "Shew" me the way?

ANNIE. Yes.

> *And now she steps out of the room—*
>
> *—but only for an instant—*
>
> *—and now here she comes in again—*
>
> *—wheeling something.*
>
> *It's a charcoal barbecue.*
>
> *You'd use it in summer for cooking hamburgers.*
>
> *She also carries several items in her arms.*
>
> *A box of Diamond Blue Tip wooden matches.*
>
> *A can of lighter fluid.*
>
> *And Paul's manuscript.*
>
> *Paul can only stare as she approaches.*
>
> *He does not believe what he sees.*
>
> *Annie takes off the lid of the barbecue, puts the manuscript into the barbecue itself where the charcoal goes—*
>
> *The barbecue is close to the bed now, very close.*

PAUL. Before, when I mentioned a snack, I was thinking more along the lines of cheese and crackers.

ANNIE. This is not a time for jokes, Paul. I've been trying to understand you. Trying to understand what made you kill Misery.

Wanting to believe that you really are good. I went back and finished the swearing book last night, at least I tried to, and I had a revelation. You must rid the world of this filth.

PAUL. You're going to burn my book?

ANNIE. No, Paul—you're going to do it.

She tosses the box of matches onto the bed.

PAUL. Annie, I've been lying on the floor all night. I need my pills.

ANNIE. And I'll get them for you. But this is first.

PAUL. Annie, can we talk about this tomorrow? I'm in so much pain I can't think straight.

ANNIE. I know this may be difficult for you.

PAUL. It's… really not difficult at all, Annie. There's stuff about publishing you don't know. I mailed a copy to my agent and by now she's made dozens of copies—every powerful publisher in New York is reading it. So if you want to burn this copy, fine—but you're not ridding the world of anything.

ANNIE. *(Just watching him.)* Then light the match.

PAUL. If that's what you want, sure.

ANNIE. Then do it.

Paul holds the box of matches—

—and he tries for a smile—

—but it won't hold—

—and worse, his hands are starting to tremble.

I know this is the only copy in the world, Paul. When you were twenty-four you wrote your first novel, but you didn't make a copy because you didn't think anyone would take you seriously. But they did. And ever since you've never made a copy because you're so superstitious—it's why you always come back here to the Silver Creek Lodge to finish your books—you told that story on Johnny Carson eleven years ago.

PAUL. Annie, this book will go to auction in New York and will sell for a lot of money… my attorney will make sure you get half of it… Nobody deserves it more than you.

ANNIE. This is not about money. It's about purity and God's values.

PAUL. You're right. I'll tell you what—I won't publish it—I'll just keep it for myself. No one will even know it exists.

Long silence now. Annie seems like she's about to agree with him.

ANNIE. As long as it does exist, your mind won't ever be free. You'll never write the books you're meant to write. I think you should light the match now.

PAUL. Annie, please listen. I know you hated the profanity, and I'm not saying you're wrong, but you've got to understand something. This book was hard to write. I quit so many times, but I kept coming back—I needed to write it. Every ambition I have as a writer is in those pages.

Pause.

It took me three years to write this book.

He stares at her.

Three years. A thousand days. If you care about me, how can you want me to destroy a thousand days?

ANNIE. It's not a very good book, Paul.

This hits Paul.

And I know good when I see it. You are good. All you need is a little help. This is the only way. God's never wrong.

Paul is silent this time. No way he can do it.

PAUL. No…

ANNIE. Paul…

PAUL. No!

ANNIE. Please let me help you, dear.

And now she flicks some drops of lighter fluid on his bed.

We're only put on this earth to help people, nothing else matters.

Now more lighter fluid flicks out.

You're so brilliant Paul, I think you'd be able to see that. *(Smiles.)* I think you do see it.

And now she flicks a few more.

And a few more.

*No question if she lit a match on the bed now, she would
probably burn him alive.*

PAUL. Annie, please don't make me do this. I'm begging you, please.

ANNIE. You can do as you choose. Do the right thing now.

Now Paul, dazed and wiped out, manages to light a match—

And drops the match on his fluid-soaked manuscript.

For a moment, nothing—

And then—and then, Jesus!—all hell explodes.

KABOOM!!! And flames leap out.

Paul can only stare. The flames grow and grow.

Goodness! GOODNESS! Heavens to Betsy!!

*They both stare at the fire. As it dies down, Annie removes
two pills from her pocket.*

Here's your Novril. Though honestly I'm giving you too much as it
is. Too much of anything can kill you.

She helps him take the pills.

How does tuna casserole sound for dinner?

PAUL. Great.

She exits. Paul spits the pills out of his mouth.

Too much of anything can kill you.

He throws the pills into the fire.

Lights transition.

Nine

Early morning. The small front porch of Annie's small house. Buster is the sheriff of the nearest town, Silver Creek. He comes up the porch, looks around a bit. Looks for a bell to ring. There is none. It is freezing out—still, he takes off his glove to prepare to knock on the door.

Annie opens the door just as he's about to knock.

ANNIE. Oh my!

BUSTER. Sorry, didn't mean to startle you. You didn't give me a chance to knock.

ANNIE. I'm not all that used to visitors out here. What can I do for you, Sheriff?

BUSTER. Ms. Wilkes, isn't it?

ANNIE. That's right.

BUSTER. I'm sorry to be bothering you so early, Ms. Wilkes. I've been going nuts with phone calls from New York—so I'm asking everyone in these parts if they've seen something. There's a writer, comes here often from New York; he was supposed to show up back home a few days ago and he didn't. Guess he checked out of the Silver Creek Lodge two weeks back, and now there's people back East scared something bad happened to him.

ANNIE. *(Shocked.)* Writer from New York? Oh my God, Paul Sheldon was staying there! He's my hero! I got all the Misery books inside. I'm just reading the new one, *Misery's Child.* Is it him you're looking for?

BUSTER. *(Shows photo.)* Yes, ma'am. Here's a photo here.

ANNIE. Oh my God. What are people saying at the Lodge?

BUSTER. Nothing unusual, ma'am. Checked out the morning of that blizzard. Said he was driving a '65 Mustang. Blue. Doubt it had chains and that was some mother of a storm—guess he coulda gone off the road near here. I was up in the helicopter yesterday and it's hard to see if a car's buried. Snow's still piled high.

ANNIE. *(Shakes her head, visibly upset.)* I don't think God would let anything bad happen to Paul Sheldon.

BUSTER. Yeah, I don't know that he's been gone long enough to worry. I told his agent when she called, maybe he decided to make a stop on his way home. Or maybe he had enough of this damn winter, went to Florida instead. But she insists he would have been in touch.

ANNIE. I have to believe he's safe. Will you let me know if you hear anything, Sheriff?

BUSTER. Oh, I think everyone will hear about it if we find him. And please, call me Buster, everyone does.

ANNIE. All my fingers are crossed for you, Buster.

> *Buster nods.*
>
> *Annie closes the porch door—very softly.*

Ten

The following dawn. But things have changed—a lot! Paul is not in bed. He is sitting—sitting in a wheelchair. A table has been set up in the corner of the room.

ANNIE. *(So excited.)* Like it so far?

PAUL. *(Manages a nod.)* I'll say—I've always wanted to visit the other side of the room.

ANNIE. Now don't poke fun—I promised you the biggest surprise of your life, remember?

PAUL. If I knew a wheelchair was my surprise I would have burned all my books.

ANNIE. That chair was expensive, even if it was secondhand. But that's only part of the surprise.

PAUL. Can I have my pills?

ANNIE. It's not time yet. Now you just sit tight while I set everything up.

Annie hurries out the door.

PAUL. I don't know how long I can sit in this chair without my Novril, Annie.

ANNIE. *(Off.)* I know it hurts now, but there will come a day—and sooner than you think—when it hurts less.

PAUL. Yeah, well, that's not today.

ANNIE. Don't be a crybaby. This is one of the most important days of your life. This is the surprise.

And she returns with an old-model typewriter.

Well? What do you think?

PAUL. It's a real antique.

ANNIE. I didn't get it for an antique. *(Indicating the table.)* It's your new studio—writers need a place to work, right?

She clunks the typewriter down on the table.

PAUL. Work? You mean write? What in the world do you think I'd write?

She has never been more excited.

ANNIE. Oh but Paul, I don't think, I know. Now that you've gotten rid of that piece of filth, you can go back to doing what you're great at—you're going to write a new novel—your greatest achievement ever— *(Big.)* MISERY'S RETURN.

Hard for Paul to answer. He just sits there.

PAUL. Annie, Misery is dead.

ANNIE. No, she's not. Even when I was so mad at you, I knew you didn't mean it when you killed her. And now you'll make it right.

An almost religious fervor now.

And this will be a book in my honor. Dedicated to me for saving your life and nursing you back to health. I'll be the very first person to read it. Oh, Paul, you're going to make me the envy of the world!

She hurries to the door again.

PAUL. *(Calling out to her.)* You just expect me to whip something off?

ANNIE. I absolutely do—I expect nothing less than your masterpiece.

PAUL. I don't have any of my notes. I have two big binders keeping track of characters, timelines, places. I don't even have any of the books.

Now she's back—this time she carries typing paper, pens, pencils, a sharpener. And all of the Misery books.

ANNIE. I have all the books, silly. Plus paper, pens, pencils, a sharpener, anything you need.

PAUL. Somehow I don't think Tolstoy wrote this way.

ANNIE. I couldn't say, you're the only genius I've ever had in this house. I have total confidence in your brilliance.

Annie opens the curtains.

Besides, the view will inspire you.

Paul looks out the window: sky, mountain, barn, open land. Desolate.

PAUL. I guess you don't get bothered by neighbors much.

ANNIE. Which is so good for you, because you can have total solitude.

PAUL. Great.

ANNIE. This is the most expensive typing paper anywhere. And I got a great deal on this fifty-pound clunker on account of the "n" key is broken—it came loose, see.

She wiggles the "n" key. Paul's eyes light up.

PAUL. Came loose, huh?

ANNIE. So she gave me five dollars off.

PAUL. Gave you? You mean you didn't dicker?

ANNIE. I might have. *(Smiles, letting him in on a secret.)* I told the saleslady "n" was one of the letters in my favorite writer's name, Paul Sheldon.

Paul smiles too.

PAUL. It's two of the letters in my favorite nurse's name—An-nie.

ANNIE. You fooler.

PAUL. *(Embarrassed—blushing.)* I'm not. Not at all.

ANNIE. *(Really wanting to please.)* Did I do good?

PAUL. You did great.

Delighted, she puts paper in the typewriter and her fingers do a little dance on the keys.

Except for just one little thing. This is Corrasable Bond—it smudges. Maybe you wouldn't mind going back into town and getting me some white, long-grained mimeo?

Pause.

ANNIE. It's a trick. You don't want to write my book so you're making up excuses not to start.

PAUL. Bring that over here, I'll show you the problem.

ANNIE. This paper cost the most so I don't see how it can smudge.

She hands him the paper and he runs his thumb over the typing.

Well, it does smudge after all—how fascinating is that?

PAUL. I thought you'd be interested. I'd like you to be in on everything, Annie—not just the finished book but how it's written.

ANNIE. I'm so touched you're thinking of me.

A wonderful smile now.

Anything else I can get for you while I'm in town? Any other crucial requirements that might need satisfying?

PAUL. Just the paper will be fine.

The smile goes—she's agitated now.

ANNIE. Are you sure? I could bring you a tape recorder—or maybe you'd like a handmade pair of writing slippers. 'Cause if you want, I'll bring back the whole store for you.

PAUL. Annie, what's the matter?

ANNIE. What's the matter? I'll tell you what's the matter. I go out of my way for you. I do everything I can to try and make you happy. I feed you, I clean you, I dress you. And what thanks do I get? "You brought the wrong paper, Annie. I can't write on this paper, Annie." Well, I'll get you your stupid paper, but you better start showing me a little more appreciation around here, Mister Man.

Suddenly she is in a rage, charging at him. She takes the ream of paper and slams it on his damaged knees. Paul's pain is both sudden and shocking, and he cries out.

32

You may think you can trick me. I know I look slow and stupid to you. But I am not stupid, Paul. And I am not slow.

Annie storms to the door, opens it, slams it shut, locks it.

Eleven

Paul does nothing. But now we realize he is doing a lot more than nothing. Paul is listening intently for any sounds from Annie. He hears the crucial sound—a car motor starting, gunning away. Paul takes a breath, gets as comfortable as he can in his wheelchair. He stares at the typewriter. He moves to it, takes a deep breath. He jiggles and removes the "n" key.

PAUL. Ha!

This is a moment of triumph—he has gotten her out of the house, and now he can try to get himself out of the room.

The key tightly in his hand, Paul wheels to the door, gets close to the lock, inserts the key, begins to unlock the door— or tries to. But the key slips from his fingers, falls to the rug.

Paul is starting to breathe more deeply now. But in something closing in on a rage, he bends way over, grabs for the key—and the gods are smiling. He lifts it, holds it tightly, inserts it back into the lock. But it's just a bitch, getting it to turn. Paul tries like hell. No good.

Harder. Still won't get it to turn. Tries again. The key turns in the lock. Paul opens the damn door.

(*Stunned.*) Sonofabitch.

And with great care he wheels out the door—the door is almost too narrow for him to make it. But he does. And as he goes through the door, for the first time...

The set changes.

Paul finds himself wheeling along a dark corridor. Ahead, it's brighter. Paul wheels toward the brightness. But slowly.

It's narrow where he finds himself—and he sure doesn't want to bang into the walls—not with his legs.

The brightness grows stronger. Paul's excitement builds.

In the hallway, Paul spots a framed, autographed picture of himself—he might sign hundreds of them a year. He picks it up and stares at it for a moment.

For the love for God.

He puts down the photo.

He spots a telephone on a small table.

Wheels to it as fast as he can.

Grabs it.

Dials.

Operator! Operator! Damn it.

Now he stops, studies the phone, turns it over. It's hollow.

You crazy bitch.

Slams the phone back down.

Now on to the kitchen. He sees a closet door—

—wheels to it excitedly—

He tries it but the door is locked.

Paul is getting desperate now.

Increasingly desperate.

The set moves again—

—only a little.

He is in the kitchen. He looks around, opens drawers. He opens all the cabinets. Inside one of them—pills.

Hello, Novril.

Stuffed.

You never saw so many pills.

Paul never did anyway.

Reaches into the pills collection.

Half stands.

This is dangerous for him.

He holds on to the arms of his wheelchair as well as he can.

Reaches high for some pills.

Too high—

—his balance begins to leave him.

Paul starts to fall—

—fall hard—

—but at the last second he manages to grab the arms of the wheelchair.

Steadies himself—

The timer on the counter goes off. Paul jumps. He struggles to turn it off, and does.

Then with all he has, he throws himself upward again—

—reaches as high as he can—

—grabs a bottle of capsules.

He reaches to the cabinet for more—just as—

The sound of Annie's car pulling in the driveway. Paul is startled.

Paul quickly closes the cabinets, begins to wheel back to the bedroom as quickly as he can.

The set moves again.

Paul wheels through the hall. Annie can be seen on the front porch, with her keys.

Paul enters his bedroom, clicks the door lock and manages to get the door closed, then stuffs the pill bottle into his sling, just as Annie enters.

Twelve

ANNIE. I've got your paper.

Paul puts his arm back in the sling.

White long-grained mimeo. Just the kind you asked for—

Paul looks up, a shaky smile on his face.

Paul, you're dripping with perspiration. Your color is very hectic.

Pause.

What have you been doing?

PAUL. You know goddamn well what I've been doing—I've been sitting here suffering. I need my pills.

ANNIE. Poor dear—you've been sitting in that chair too long. Let me get you back into bed, and then I'll give them to you.

PAUL. *(A child's tantrum.)* I want my pills now! Please make my pain go away, Annie.

ANNIE. It'll only take a second.

PAUL. No, please make my pain go away, Annie.

She looks at him.

ANNIE. It just breaks my heart to see you like this. Here you go.

She gives him two Novril and turns away to pour a glass of water. As her back is turned, Paul puts the pills in his sling.

She returns and Paul pretends to swallow the pills.

Now let's get you into bed…

PAUL. No! No. I'm sorry I panicked. I'll feel better, now that I've had these. Now that you're back. This paper looks perfect. I'd like to do some writing now.

ANNIE. Well I am so happy to hear that.

PAUL. Can you open the paper for me?

She opens the paper.

Annie, if I write this story for you…

ANNIE. Novel!

PAUL. I'll write it, and I'll go home?

ANNIE. I think that by the time you finish, you should be up to the strain of meeting people again. Is that what you wanted to hear? So, agreed?

PAUL. Agreed.

> *She begins to wheel him to the typewriter.*

ANNIE. Think of me as your inspiration.

PAUL. Oh, I do.

ANNIE. Just remember this. Now and forever. I'll treasure whatever you write. I have faith in you...

> *Beat.*

my darling...

> *She leaves him.*
>
> *Paul lets out an enormous sigh of relief.*
>
> *Then he gets to work.*
>
> *He takes the loose pills from his sling. He opens one capsule and tastes it. Then he puts the pills in the bottle with the rest.*
>
> *Next, he takes a piece of paper and folds it into an envelope. Suddenly, Annie enters, and he quickly hides what he's doing.*

Is everything okay? I don't hear typing.

PAUL. *(Quickly hiding the envelope.)* Great! It's great. Just getting started.

> *She exits.*
>
> *Paul begins to type...*

MISERY'S RETUR No "n".

> *He continues typing.*

BY PAUL SHELDO
FOR A—no "n," no "n"—IE WILKES

> *He stares at the paper.*

(As he types this.) Fuckfuckfuckfuckfuck. Fuck. Fuck. Fuckfuckfuck.

> *The lights shift...*

Thirteen

Now it's hours later. Paul sits working. There are several pages on the table beside him.

Annie enters—she holds papers in her hands.

ANNIE. I'm sorry, Paul, but this is not right. You'll have to do it over again.

PAUL. *(Stunned.)* You don't like it? What happened to "I'll treasure whatever you do"?

ANNIE. Like it? Of course I like it—it's beautiful! But it's not right. Throw it all out. Except for the part of naming Gravedigger Wilkes after me, you can leave that in.

PAUL. Maybe you're being a little hasty here?

ANNIE. Paul—what you've written just isn't fair.

PAUL. Fair? How is it not fair? It's Misery, alive, just like you asked for!

ANNIE. Remember, Ian did ride for Dr. Cleary at the end of the last book, that's okay, but his horse fell jumping that fence and Ian broke his shoulder and he never reached the doctor. So this book can't start with an "experimental blood transfusion" that saves her life, because she was dead and buried in the ground. You cheated.

PAUL. I wouldn't call that cheating—

ANNIE. When I was growing up in Bakersfield my favorite thing in the whole wide world was to go to movies on Saturday afternoons for the chapter plays—

PAUL. *(Cutting in.)* —cliffhangers—

ANNIE. *(Suddenly angry.)* —I know that Mister Man! They also call them chapter plays—I'm not stupid, you know.

> *Beat.*

Anyway, my favorite was *Rocket Man* and once it was a no-brakes chapter—the bad guys stuck him in a car on a mountain road and knocked him out and—

She is back in her childhood more strongly now.

—and welded the doors shut and tore out the brakes and started him to his doom and he woke up and tried to steer and tried to get out but the car went off a cliff before he could escape and it crashed and burned—

She's remembering it all so clearly.

—and I was so upset and excited and the next week you better believe I was first in line and they always start with the end of the last week and there was Rocket Man trying to get out and here came the cliff and JUST BEFORE the car went off he jumped free and all the kids cheered— *(More powerful now.)* — but I didn't cheer, I stood right up and started shouting, "This isn't what happened last week—have you all got amnesia? Are you too stupid to remember?—THEY JUST CHEATED US—THIS WASN'T FAIR—" *(Shouting now.)* "He was in the car when it went over! HE DIDN'T GET OUT OF THE COCKADOODIE CAR!"

PAUL. —they always cheated like that in cliff— *(Stops himself.)* — in chapter plays.

ANNIE. But not you. Not with my Misery. Misery was buried in the ground at the end of the last book, Paul, so you'll have to start from there.

Pause.

Do you understand?

PAUL. Yes.

He does understand; she is right.

Yes.

ANNIE. Then you know what's wrong?

PAUL. I do. But I don't know if I know how to fix it.

There is a long pause, as Annie heads toward the door. She hesitates, then turns around.

ANNIE. Well, put your thinking cap on. This is exciting, don't you think so?

PAUL. I think if it was easy to write a book, everybody would do it.

ANNIE. Maybe it was a bee.

PAUL. What?

ANNIE. Maybe it was a bee.

Paul looks at her. She blushes red.

I saw it once at the hospital. Sometimes a beesting can cause a comatose condition which can make a person seem dead. Similar to a cataleptic state.

She is embarrassed.

Oh gosh, you're the writer, not me. Just forget I said anything. I'm sorry.

PAUL. Don't be sorry—

But she closes the door and is gone, her footsteps hurrying towards to the kitchen.

Long pause as he considers this, rejects it, considers it again, turning over ideas in his head, rejecting, combining, connecting. Then, it hits.

Holy shit. Goddamnit, Annie.

Paul reaches for the paper. Puts it in the machine. Still working through his thought, he begins to type, slowly. It feels different than when he started earlier. His typing gets a bit faster. He removes his sling with some pain and continues typing, faster now, with both hands. It gains some momentum. He types and types, as the sun begins to rise.

Fourteen

Now it's bright sunlight. Paul sits at the table. He is very tired and very nervous. Annie sits across the room studying some typed pages. Now she looks at him—hard to tell what she's thinking.

PAUL. Well? Should I keep going?

Annie suddenly looks as joyous as we've yet seen her.

ANNIE. I'll kill you if you don't, Mister Man! *(Building into a fervor.)* —Oh, Paul, when Ian realized that the reason they'd buried Misery alive was because a beesting had put her in a temporary coma—

(Even bigger.) —and when Gravedigger Wilkes remembered how thirty years earlier, the same thing had happened to Lady Evelyn-Hyde and then old Doctor Cleary deduced that Misery must be Lady Evelyn-Hyde's long-lost daughter because of the rarity of deadly beestings—well, my heart just leapt!

Paul watches her—it's as if he had nothing to do with it.

I've known from the very first book that Misery had to be born of nobility—and I was right!

PAUL. And it's fair?

ANNIE. Yes. It's fair. And it's exciting. But it's gruesome too. Misery's bloody hands scratching to get out of her coffin… It's not like any of the other Misery books.

PAUL. Well, different circumstances.

Annie touches the pages with such gentleness.

ANNIE. I'm wild to know what happens next. Will she be her old self now that Ian has dug her out or will she have amnesia?

PAUL. Have to wait.

ANNIE. Will she still love him with that special perfect love?

PAUL. Have to wait.

ANNIE. *(Pleading.)* Not even a hint?

Pause.

PAUL. It's good, isn't it?

This is a very big moment for Paul.

Annie begins to spin around the room like a happy child.

ANNIE. Misery's alive. Misery's alive! Oh, this house is going to be filled with romance—I'm going to play all my Liberace records for us! Oh, Paul, can I read each chapter when you finish?—Please, please, please—it would be almost like the chapter plays when I was a kid. I could fill in all the "n"s for you.

PAUL. Only on the condition that you do something for me?

ANNIE. What?

PAUL. Would you have dinner with me tonight?

She is stunned, thrilled, can't speak.

41

To celebrate Misery's return—I could never have done it without you.

ANNIE. Oh Paul—It would be an honor.

And she dashes excitedly out of the room.

PAUL. *(A whisper.)* Please, God…

We stay locked on Paul, as the lights fade.

Fifteen

Liberace begins to sing for us.

Louder than he's yet been.

Lights up on the kitchen.

Annie has set up a table with her best silverware and china. There are wine glasses, a bottle of Gallo red wine.

The whole place is as romantic as Annie can make anything.

And Annie—we've never seen her dolled up like this. She wheels Paul to the table.

ANNIE. I hope you like it.

PAUL. This looks wonderful.

He takes one.

And you look very pretty.

Annie starts to reply, is too embarrassed, stops.

ANNIE. *(Delighted, almost shy.)* Well I'm not going to tell you what you can say.

The awkward silence goes on.

PAUL. Where did you get a dress like that?

ANNIE. It was my mother's. It's old-fashioned.

PAUL. I like it, it's modest.

ANNIE. It is modest. I don't mean to pry, but I read in *People* magazine that you were seeing that model who does those disgusting jeans commercials. And I said it can't be true. Paul Sheldon would never waste his time with a trampy woman like that.

42

PAUL. Well, you can't believe everything you read in *People* magazine.

ANNIE. I knew it. I knew it wasn't true.

> *Beat.*

PAUL. You know, when I was a kid, nurses were my heart's desire.

> *Annie is dumbfounded, cannot speak.*

The uniform was part of it, I'm sure, but not just that. Who knows, maybe I just wanted someone kind to take care of me. The way you're taking care of me now.

> *After a moment—*

I bet you were something in your nurse's uniform.

> *Annie, again, cannot speak. They eat. There is awkward silence as they chew.*

Wine?

> *He lifts the bottle, and begins to fill her glass with red wine. Annie blushes and tries to put her hand over the glass.*

ANNIE. Oh no, no, no, no.

> *Paul succeeds in pouring her a large glass of wine. Annie sheepishly accepts. He pours himself a glass. They look at one another. Paul smiles. Then he takes a bite of food.*

PAUL. I have never, not in all my life, eaten meatloaf to compare with this—WOW—

ANNIE. Well, I have a secret—I only use fresh tomatoes—and to give it that little extra zip, I mix in some Spam with the ground beef.

PAUL. You cannot get this in a New York restaurant, that's for sure.

> *She is thrilled, does her best to hide it.*

ANNIE. It was my mother's recipe.

PAUL. You must have been very close with her.

ANNIE. Yes, I was. In my whole life, she was the only person who never let me down. Well, her and Misery.

PAUL. Annie?

> *She manages to look at him.*

I think we should have a toast.

ANNIE. A toast?

43

PAUL. Yes. To Misery.

ANNIE. To Misery.

PAUL. No, wait—let's do this right—do you have any candles?

ANNIE. I don't know—I think maybe somewhere I do—

She gets up, hurries out the door.

The instant she's gone, Paul pulls out the envelope filled with Novril powder. He empties it into her glass of wine as he talks.

PAUL. It's great to see the rest of the house. I'd imagined it was lovely but I didn't expect this. Did you study decorating or do you just have a flair?

ANNIE. *(Out of the room but we can hear her clearly.)* You fooler— but I guess you could say I picked things up over the years.

PAUL. Well, it certainly says you. *(Louder.)* Listen, if you can't find any, it's OK—I just thought it might be nice.

Annie reenters now with a candle.

ANNIE. Are you kidding?—if anyone ever told me that there would come a day when I'd be having a candlelit dinner with Paul Sheldon—and in my own home—well I would have checked both legs to see which one was being pulled.

She holds the candle out toward him.

Will this do?

PAUL. It's perfect.

She puts the candle on the table, lights it.

Paul raises his glass to toasting position.

To Misery and to Annie Wilkes—who brought her back to life.

Annie raises her glass now.

ANNIE. Oh Paul...

There is just an instant before they touch glasses—

—and she knocks over the candle—

—accidentally knocks over her glass—

—spilling the wine.

(Wiping up the spilled wine with her napkin.) Oh God Paul, what

have I done? *(Humiliated.)* I ruined your beautiful toast—can you find it in your heart to forgive me? *(Reaches for the Gallo.)* Let me pour another glass. *(She does.)* Can we both please pretend this never happened? *(Toasting position now.)* To Misery.

PAUL. Misery.

> *They drink their wine.*
>
> *Liberace sings on.*
>
> *Lights dim.*

Sixteen

> *Days have passed. Paul sits at his desk, typing furiously. He's in it… escaping into the page. He is surrounded by pages. Annie comes in with a vanilla ice cream sundae. He does not see or hear her at first.*

ANNIE. I wanted to bring you something special. I made you an ice cream sundae. You've been working so hard, you deserve it.

> *He doesn't touch it. Keeps typing.*

You better eat it before it melts.

PAUL. *(Still not looking up from typewriter.)* Why don't you eat it. I'm right in the middle of a sentence.

> *She regards him in awe.*

ANNIE. What part are you working on?

PAUL. Excuse me?

ANNIE. You haven't given me new pages in a week, so I don't know anything that's happened since that mysterious stranger showed up at the inn! Is it Misery's real father?

PAUL. Annie, can we talk about this later?

ANNIE. *(Reaching for the stack of papers.)* Okay, well I'll just take these new chapters then and fill in the "n"s.

PAUL. *(Putting his hand on the stack.)* No thanks, I've actually been doing it myself.

ANNIE. Why? I didn't do a good job?

PAUL. You did fine. I mean, you missed a couple. But that's fine.

ANNIE. Well, maybe I can just sit here and watch you work. I'll be quiet.

PAUL. I can't write with someone else in the room.

ANNIE. I'm not "someone." I'm your number one fan. I had the idea about the bee. That helped you when you were stuck.

PAUL. Annie, I got the idea for Misery's kidnapping from something the TV repair guy said. It's not the suggestion of an idea, it's what you do with it.

ANNIE. Well, I knew writers were supposed to have big egos but I didn't understand that meant ingratitude, too.

PAUL. I'm not ungrateful, Annie. I'm focused. I only have a few chapters to go—in a couple of weeks I'll be done.

ANNIE. I just wanna know one thing. Did the Baron kill her father? That's one thing I've got to know or I'll go crazy.

PAUL. I'm not going to tell you anything.

ANNIE. I made you a sundae, you can tell me one thing.

PAUL. Do you want me to finish the book, or sit here and have a nice chat.

ANNIE. Don't take that sarcastic tone with me.

PAUL. Then don't pretend you don't understand what I'm saying! Now I'm right in the middle of a major scene, and the more you talk, the harder it is for me to write.

He turns back to the typewriter.

Dammit. Well, there you go—now I lost it.

Pause.

ANNIE. Are you going to eat your ice cream?

PAUL. I'm not hungry.

ANNIE. I've upset you. I'm sorry. I expect that you're right. I was wrong to ask.

Annie gathers up the ice cream bowl, proudly admitting her mistake.

PAUL. Please shut the door on your way out.

> *Annie exits, shutting the door.*

And if you're going to bribe me, try bourbon.

> *Paul smiles.*
>
> *Victory!*
>
> *When he can no longer hear Annie's footsteps, he begins to bench press the typewriter several times above his head.*
>
> *Finally, as a thunderstorm begins, the lights shift, indicating the passage of time.*

Seventeen

> *Weeks have passed. The stack of papers next to Paul's typewriter has grown. So has his strength. The storm grows louder, and louder.*
>
> *Louder still.*
>
> *The rumbles are deafening.*
>
> *Now lightning flashes begin.*
>
> *We can make out Paul.*
>
> *—And now Annie has entered.*
>
> *Lumbering like a robot.*
>
> *She wears slippers and an old housecoat.*
>
> *Her hair is more straggling that we've seen it. There is food on her housecoat. Her eyes are dead.*
>
> *She moves to Paul.*
>
> *Lightning!*
>
> *Annie stands in the doorway. She is watching him. This goes on for a while. He finally senses her, sees her.*

PAUL. Annie? What is it?

ANNIE. The rain, it gives me the blues.

Now she just stares at Paul in silence.

PAUL. This is more than the rain.

ANNIE. Right—it's you.

PAUL. Go on.

ANNIE. When you first came here, I only loved the part of Paul Sheldon that made such wonderful stories, because that's the only part I had. But now I know I love the rest of him too.

She moves closer to the window now.

I know you don't love me—don't say you do. You're a beautiful brilliant famous man of the world and I'm… I'm not a movie-star type. *(Sadder and sadder.)* You'll never know the fear of losing someone like you if you're someone like me.

PAUL. Why would you lose me?

ANNIE. The book is almost finished—your legs are getting stronger—soon you'll be able to walk. Then you'll be wanting to leave.

PAUL. But I like it here.

ANNIE. Thank you for saying that, but we both know it's not altogether true.

Beat.

You are not a stupid man, Paul. You know I can never let you leave. You've known for some time, haven't you?

Annie removes an old pistol from her sweater pocket.

I could end this now for both of us. Maybe the next world is better.

PAUL. This book is almost finished, Annie. Don't you want to see how it all turns out. Don't you want to know?

ANNIE. I DO want to know. More than anything on earth, I want to know how it comes out.

Beat.

I think I better get out for a while. I might put bullets in it.

And like a robot, she slowly crosses the room, goes out the door.

Paul, stunned, just lies there.

He keeps on listening.

Now the sound of the front door closing and locking.

Paul doesn't move.

Now the more distant sound of the car starting, gunning into the night.

Lights fade to black on Paul, thinking.

Eighteen

Lights up on the kitchen, which is no longer well kept in pristine order, but a mess: overflowing bags of trash, rotting food, etc. Paul wheels himself in. He takes it all in, wheeling himself about… it is frightening.

In despair, in the kitchen, amid the trash, he finds a long kitchen knife. He practices hiding it in his sling and then wielding it.

PAUL. See you in the morning.

He takes the knife and wheels back to his room.

The thunder is worse than ever.

The thunder is painful.

After what could be minutes, could be hours, Annie enters the kitchen.

She surveys the mess for a while, and exits.

Nineteen

In the dark, thunder and lightning. Then, lights up on Paul's room. It is a beautiful day. The storm is over. "Moonlight Sonata" plays. Liberace has never been more romantic. *

Paul sleeps.

Annie is standing there by his bed. Paul blinks, tries to move—

—but he's groggy—

—helpless—

—He has been strapped to his bed.

Annie stands there, bright-eyed and bushy-tailed.

ANNIE. Hi, Punkin.

> *Paul manages a nod.*

Guess what?—I know you've been out.

PAUL. What… What are you talking about? What's going on?

ANNIE. You've been out of your room.

PAUL. No I haven't. Annie, what is this?

ANNIE. You've been out at least twice. I warned you not to try to trick me, Paul.

> *Paul says nothing, just stares at her, waiting. Annie walks slowly back to the foot of the bed.*

PAUL. I don't know what you're talking about.

ANNIE. You left marks with the wheelchair the first time you got out. I know there's Novril missing. And you shouldn't have turned off the timer, Paul. At first I was so confused as to how in the world you got out, then last night I found your key.

> *Now she holds up the typewriter key.*

PAUL. Okay, I went out the two times, once because YOU left me here in pain and I needed pills, and the other to get water so I didn't die of thirst.

---

* See Note on Songs/Recordings at the back of this volume.

ANNIE. I suppose you never tried the doors, or the phone?

PAUL. Sure I did, but you know the phone doesn't work and the doors are locked, and where am I going?

ANNIE. So you went out twice, once for pills and once for water.

PAUL. Yes, Annie, that's it, I swear.

ANNIE. You're lying to me. But that's okay, Paul.

> *Beat.*

Looking for this?

> *Annie pulls out the knife. Paul knows the jig is up.*

I found this right in the bed before I gave you your pre-op shot.

PAUL. Pre-op?

ANNIE. Last night it became so clear. Would you ever really want to stay? I had to ask myself that. And as much as I wanted to pull the wool over my own eyes, I suppose I knew the answer even before I found your key.

> *She holds up the typewriter "n" key.*

Paul, do you know about the early days at the Kimberly Diamond Mine? Do you know what they did to the native workers who stole diamonds? Now don't you worry, they didn't kill them—that would be like junking a Mercedes just because it had a broken spring.

> *She is building to climax now.*

No, if they caught them, they had to make sure they could go on working—but they also had to make sure they could never run away. What they did was called hobbling.

> *And with that she reaches down out of sight and comes up holding a block of wood.*

PAUL. Annie—whatever you're thinking about doing, please don't do it.

> *Annie wedges the block firmly between his legs just above the ankles, secures it and adjusts his feet.*

ANNIE. Now don't fuss. I gave you a shot of Fentanyl to relax you.

PAUL. Why would I run away? I'm a writer, Annie—it's all I am—and I've never written this well—even you said that this is my best, didn't you? Didn't you? Why would I leave a place where I'm doing my best work? It doesn't make any sense.

ANNIE. Now, don't fuss.

Annie picks up a sledgehammer.

PAUL. Annie, I promise I'll never leave my room again. I'll stay here forever. Annie, I'll be good, I swear, I'll be good! Please, PLEASE, please, I'm begging you, don't do this. I'll be good!

She pulls the sledgehammer back—

ANNIE. Darling trust me, it's for the best.

—gets ready to strike.

PAUL. Annie, for God's sake please!

ANNIE. Darling, relax... I'm a trained nurse.

And with that, she swings the sledgehammer against his right ankle—

—there is the sound of metal crushing bone—

Paul's scream is terrifying.

Almost done—just one more.

She swings the sledgehammer against his other ankle.

God I love you.

Paul cannot stop screaming. The set rotates.

Twenty

A week later. Annie's front porch. It's spring now. Annie opens the door, and the TV is on loudly in the background.

ANNIE. Sheriff?

BUSTER. Hope I'm not interrupting. I tried calling but there was never an answer, phone just rang and rang.

ANNIE. Oh goodness, I turn the TV up full volume, my hearing is not what it used to be—I'll never hear the phone when *M.A.S.H.* is on! Do you like *M.A.S.H.*?

BUSTER. I don't watch much TV.

ANNIE. Oh, well...

She closes the front door.

What can I do for you, Sheriff?

BUSTER. I felt I should come by, ma'am. When I was here in February, you told me Paul Sheldon was your hero.

ANNIE. Is my hero. *(Excited.)* Oh my God—you're here to tell me you found him?

BUSTER. No ma'am. We didn't find him, but we did find his car. Crashed it off the side of a hill, just a few miles from here. The snow's all melted that way now. Looked like it sat at the bottom of the hill for months.

ANNIE. Are you telling me he's dead?

BUSTER. Well, I can't say for sure, ma'am, but the FBI is one hundred percent sure. They found his car and told me he must have crawled out after the crash and died.

ANNIE. But you don't think so?

BUSTER. Oh most likely they're right. They're the FBI. I thought the car door looked like it may have been pried open, but that didn't add up to them. They think—he couldn't have gotten too far if he was injured, and the body would have to be close by. But since we haven't found a body, I figured there's really only one explanation.

He lets that hang there a moment.

ANNIE. What's that?

BUSTER. The coyotes got to him.

ANNIE. No! Please, please no!

BUSTER. I hate being the one to tell you all this. Pete at the general store tells me you really are Paul Sheldon's biggest fan. Says you have him set the first copy aside for you every time a new novel comes out.

ANNIE. I told you as much.

BUSTER. Well, at least you got to see him in town.

ANNIE. I never saw him. I'd certainly remember if I had.

BUSTER. That's right, you said that.

ANNIE. I'm sure he came here for peace and quiet and not to be bothered by the likes of us.

BUSTER. It's strange, both of them coming to an end at the same time.

ANNIE. Both of them?

BUSTER. Paul Sheldon and Misery.

She keeps looking at him.

Oh… I picked up Mr. Sheldon's last Misery book. Read the whole thing.

ANNIE. You did? What did you think?

BUSTER. Sure came as a shock to me, Misery dying like that at the end. Didn't see that coming.

ANNIE. Misery's not dead.

BUSTER. How's that?

ANNIE. Misery's not dead, Sheriff. I just know it.

Pause.

BUSTER. Well, I don't think there'll be any more books, Ms. Wilkes.

ANNIE. There already is.

Buster looks back at her.

As his number one fan, I know he would never have left the Lodge unless he'd finished a new book. So when he turns up, or when you find his body, you'll find the next Misery.

BUSTER. I hope you're right about that.

ANNIE. I'm certain. And you should read the whole series. From the beginning.

BUSTER. Well maybe I'll do that. You stay out of trouble now.

She turns and goes into the house.

Twenty-One

Daylight. Paul's room. He lies in bed.

Liberace sings softly.

Annie enters quietly.

ANNIE. Can't sleep all day, Punkin.

Paul barely stirs. He has been in bed all week.

Give us a smile?

PAUL. *(Giving her the finger.)* Here's one.

ANNIE. Such a cutie.

PAUL. *(And now the other finger.)* Here's another one.

No question, Paul is a lot stronger now than he has been.

ANNIE. No more jokes, Paul—it's time for you to get back to your writing—it's been more than a week and I've been patient.

PAUL. It's weird, but for some reason, a couple of crushed ankles haven't done that much for my creative juices. Now, as the French are so fond of saying, "get the fuck out of here."

ANNIE. The sheriff just paid me a visit.

Paul cannot help but look over at her.

Oh, that got you, didn't it. Well, news flash, Mister Man. The FBI thinks you're dead. It's just you and me now, Paul.

Beat.

You owe me your life. I know you'll keep that in mind. You need to start writing again.

Pause.

PAUL. I figured out the ending. Want me to tell you what happens?

ANNIE. Be careful, Paul.

Annie looks at him.

PAUL. I think you're really going to dig this. Misery and Ian get into a big fight, I'm sure you know the drill; "I never loved you, blah, blah, blah." She storms out and takes Barkley with her... you know,

Barkley, her dog, her big Irish setter… well, they go to a hotel. An inn. At the bar, over a few drinks, she tells Barkley how awful Ian is. One thing leads to another, they head upstairs and well, can you guess what happens? She fucks her dog!

ANNIE. You are less than charming today.

PAUL. What are you going to do about it? Kill me? I dare you.

ANNIE. I'll drive a sledgehammer into your man gland if you're not nicer.

PAUL. Be my guest.

>*And he spreads his legs.*

ANNIE. That is so disgusting— *(Then resolved.)* I can make you write it.

PAUL. Can you?

>*They stare at each other. Impasse.*

>*After a moment—the sound of knocking on the porch door.*

ANNIE. You say one fucking word.

>*Annie's hand goes over Paul's mouth as he lets out a muffled scream. She grabs Paul's arm. Annie takes the cap off a hypodermic needle.*

>*He struggles with her—hard—keeping her arm at bay, getting his hands around his neck to strangle her.*

>*But she's the more desperate, jams the needle in.*

I don't understand you.

>*Paul continues to struggle until…*

>*Paul's eyes close—whatever she injected him with takes effect.*

When are we going to develop a sense of trust?

>*She checks him. He's out.*

>*Annie tears out of the room—*

>*—and the set moves.*

Twenty-Two

The set turns. Annie opens the door to find Buster there, all business.

BUSTER. May I come in?

ANNIE. You must think I've got no manners. Please—

Buster enters with her to the kitchen.

I made some coffee—let me get you some.

BUSTER. There's something I forgot to ask you. When I was talking to Pete at the general store he also mentioned you've become the biggest customer he ever had for typing paper. I'm hoping you can explain that to me.

Annie looks away from Buster for a moment. Then she starts to speak, very quietly.

And so sad.

ANNIE. You must never tell anyone what I'm about to tell you.

BUSTER. Depends if you're breaking the law.

ANNIE. *(Fighting back tears.)* When you told me that Paul Sheldon was missing, that he was most likely out there frozen to death or worse, I got down on my knees and I prayed. *(Shaking her head.)* And while I was down on my knees, God answered me.

Buster is caught up in her story—this is not what he'd been expecting.

God told me to get ready.

BUSTER. For what?

ANNIE. To try and be Paul Sheldon's replacement. He said he has given so much pleasure to so many people and there's a shortage of pleasure on this planet these days, in case you hadn't noticed.

Annie is fighting back tears but she manages to get her words out.

God told me that, "Since you are his number one fan in all the universe, you should make up new stories as if you were Paul Sheldon." *(Harder to speak.)* I said to God, "I don't think I can do that. I've never once in my life thought I could tell stories." And God said to me, "You must try."

She is so moved now.

So I've been trying. I went to town and I bought the same kind of paper that Paul Sheldon wrote on. And a clunky old typewriter that didn't even have an "n"—and every day, Buster, I have been working so hard. I know the kind of words he used. I know the kind of stories he told. *(Heartbreaking.)* But I have no talent!

Buster says nothing, just studies her.

I spend day after day trying—I've written two hundred pages and it's agony.

BUSTER. That many?

ANNIE. Want to read them? Maybe you could help me.

BUSTER. *(Slow shake of his head.)* Never been much of a critic. But you sure are Paul Sheldon's number one fan. Maybe I could pay you a visit again sometime?

ANNIE. I'd be delighted.

She shows Buster out.

And now at last, Paul is awake—

—He sees the water pitcher—

—grabs the water pitcher—

bangs it loudly against the window. From outside, Buster's voice is heard.

BUSTER. *(Shouting.)* Ms. Wilkes? *(Louder.)* Annie—answer me. Are you all right?

PAUL. *(Doing his best to shout.)* In here. In here. IN HERE—

Buster throws the door open—

—and is stunned to see the man lying in bed.

BUSTER. Oh my God—it's you—Paul Sheldon—you're alive—

—but too late.

There is a sudden incredibly loud explosion—

—and Buster, blood-covered and very dead, falls to the floor.

Then, Annie is in the doorway, holding a very large shotgun.

Annie moves a step into the room. She is clearly expert with her shotgun.

ANNIE. If it's not one thing, it's another.

Annie drags Buster's body off as Paul can only stare, in shock. Annie returns.

I'm sorry you had to see that, Paul, and I'm sorry we won't have time to finish the book.

Beat.

I have two bullets, one for you and one for me. Now don't be afraid. I love you.

PAUL. I know you do.

Pause.

And I love you too.

This stops her.

And you're right—we have no choice but to die. *(Passionately now.)* But you were chosen to save me for a reason. The world believes Misery is dead. You and I have the power to give Misery eternal life. We have to finish the book.

ANNIE. But there's no time—you don't think they'll come look for him?

PAUL. We have time. They won't look for him until morning. Let me finish. By dawn we'll give Misery back to the world.

Annie hesitates a long moment, thinking—then she puts on the safety, and lowers the gun.

Twenty-Three

Paul typing—the sound is thunderous.

Now his table light goes on.

Paul is concentrating desperately on his work. His lips move but he's not even aware of it.

Annie is on the bed, reading pages.

ANNIE. The stranger staying at the inn, is he someone from Misery's past? Is it her father? I know it's her father…! But who is he? He is right about to turn around and she is going to see his face for the first time! Who is it, Paul??

PAUL. You'll know soon enough. I'm starting the last page and the answer will be there.

ANNIE. This will be our legacy.

PAUL. It will.

ANNIE. Oh Paul, for Misery to be happy… That's all I ever wanted.

PAUL. I want to give you an ending worthy of everything you've done for me, Annie. When I finish this page, everything has to be perfect. I'll need three things.

ANNIE. I know what they are. *(Ticking them off.)* You need one cigarette because you used to smoke but you quit except when you finish a book and you just have one. And you need a book of matches. And you need one glass of champagne. *(Thinks.)* Dome Pear-igg-non.

PAUL. Dome Pear-igg-non it is.

> *Annie hurriedly exits, leaving the pages she was reading.*
>
> *Paul finishes typing the last page. He carefully stacks the rest of the book now, getting everything squared away.*
>
> *Now here comes Annie, carrying a tray—*
>
> *—it has one cigarette, matches, a bottle of Dom Pérignon, and a glass.*
>
> *She puts it down on his typing table.*

ANNIE. Did I do good?

PAUL. You did perfect—except this time we're going to need two glasses.

ANNIE. Oh, Paul, this is even more romantic than our dinner.

> *And off she goes.*
>
> *The instant she is out of the room, Paul sets to work.*
>
> *He dumps the book in his wastebasket—grabs the matches—*
>
> *—and soon his book is burning!*
>
> *He takes the final page out of the typewriter, and holds it above the flame.*
>
> *Then, as Annie comes to the door—*

PAUL. Remember how for all those years no one ever knew who Misery's father was? Want to know, Annie? It's right here.

ANNIE. Paul—you can't!

PAUL. Why not?—I learned it from you.

> *He thrusts the final page into the fire.*

ANNIE. Not MISERY—NOT MY MISERY!

> *She charges, drops to her knees by the burning wastebasket—*
>
> *—does her best to stop the fire.*
>
> *Now Paul does something we have seen him do—*
>
> *He lifts the typewriter above his head—*
>
> *—Annie kneels beneath him, fighting the flames.*
>
> *Paul screams—*
>
> *He's in a wild rage—*
>
> *And now he slams the typewriter right down into her face.*
>
> *Blood spurts.*
>
> *Everywhere.*
>
> *Now it's Annie's turn to scream.*
>
> *The blood won't stop.*
>
> *The flames burn on.*
>
> *Annie smashes into the floor.*

We think it's over for Annie. Paul does too.

But then suddenly, she is up... lunging for him in his chair...

You lying son of a bitch!

Paul springs out of his wheelchair and lands with a thud on the floor. Annie grabs him by the ankle, twisting hard.

They are rolling around on the floor, pulling at one another.

Paul begins to shove the charred paper in her mouth. Annie fights to hold his hand away.

PAUL. You want it? Eat it, eat it till you choke, you sick twisted fuck.

Annie grabs the paper, and with his now free hand Paul grabs her neck, choking her. Annie struggles, until, finally... it is all, all, over.

Blackout.

Darkness.

The darkness lingers.

Epilogue

Now at last there is light—

—and we are no longer in Annie's house.

We are on a stage.

In New York City.

ANNOUNCER. *(Offstage.)* Ladies and gentlemen, please welcome the best-selling author of the Misery Chastain series, Paul Sheldon.

And here comes Paul.

He looks great.

He wears slacks and a blazer.

And he is walking to the front of the stage.

Walking!

It is the first time we have seen Paul walk.

He walks with a limp.

PAUL. Thank you, everyone. I missed the book tour for *Misery's Child* so it's especially nice to kick off the tour for *Misery's Return* here at home in New York City.

Beat.

I had hoped to be touring with a different book this fall, but life has a way of shifting gears on us. That book feels very far away now, part of another life.

Beat.

I do know that I'm very happy to be able to share *Misery's Return* with you. And I suspect most of you have heard something of the circumstances by which I came to do so. If hiding the real manuscript and destroying a decoy sounds like something out of a gothic novel, well, what can I say... I am a man of my genre.

Beat.

Writing this book saved my life, and so I had to save this book. I wrote it for a woman who believed in my characters more than I did, who demanded that I be fair to them. She needed to know what would happen next in the story, and to my surprise, I discovered that I did too.

Beat.

My daughter, Chloe, who I'm delighted is here tonight, asked me what I'll write next. And I honestly don't know. My agent thinks I should write about my experiences in Colorado, but I don't think that's possible. Not yet. I do know I'm a different writer than I was. I think maybe I'm a better writer because of the... experience of writing this book. Better because I finally understand the kind of writer I'm supposed to be. And for that, I owe something, I owe someone... And so the dedication remains, FOR A—no "n," no "n"—IE WILKES.

> *Annie appears, an apparition, bloody and holding the sledgehammer.*
>
> *Paul freezes, stares for a moment, takes a deep breath, tries desperately to recover his poise.*

Whatever awaits me I like to think I… I hope I… All we can do is move forward, right? All we can do is move on.

ANNIE. I'll never leave you, Paul. I'm your number one fan.

> *Paul can only stare, shaken.*
>
> *Annie laughs.*
>
> *Lights fade to black.*
>
> *Final curtain.*

End of Play

PROPERTY LIST

(Use this space to create props lists for your production)

SOUND EFFECTS
(Use this space to create sound effects lists for your production)

Dear reader,

Thank you for supporting playwrights by purchasing this acting edition! You may not know that Dramatists Play Service was founded, in 1936, by the Dramatists Guild and a number of prominent play agents to protect the rights and interests of playwrights. To this day, we are still a small company committed to our partnership with the Guild, and by proxy all playwrights, established and aspiring, working in the English language.

Because of our status as a small, independent publisher, we respectfully reiterate that this text may not be distributed or copied in any way, or uploaded to any file-sharing sites, including ones you might think are private. Photocopying or electronically distributing books means both DPS and the playwright are not paid for the work, and that ultimately hurts playwrights everywhere, as our profits are shared with the Guild.

We also hope you want to perform this play! Plays are wonderful to read, but even better when seen. If you are interested in performing or producing the play, please be aware that performance rights must be obtained through Dramatists Play Service. This is true for *any* public performance, even if no one is getting paid or admission is not being charged. Again, playwrights often make their sole living from performance royalties, so performing plays without paying the royalty is ultimately a loss for a real writer.

This acting edition is the **only approved text for performance**. There may be other editions of the play available for sale from other publishers, but DPS has worked closely with the playwright to ensure this published text reflects their desired text of all future productions. If you have purchased a revised edition (sometimes referred to as other types of editions, like "Broadway Edition," or "[Year] Edition"), that is the only edition you may use for performance, unless explicitly stated in writing by Dramatists Play Service.

Finally, this script cannot be changed without written permission from Dramatists Play Service. If a production intends to change the script in any way—including casting against the writer's intentions for characters, removing or changing "bad" words, or making other cuts however small—without permission, they are breaking the law. And, perhaps more importantly, changing an artist's work. Please don't do that!

We are thrilled that this play has made it into your hands. We hope you love it as much as we do, and thank you for helping us keep the American theater alive and vital.

Note on Songs/Recordings, Images, or Other Production Design Elements

The song "I'll Be Seeing You," and any recordings thereof, are under copyright. Please look at your performance license or contact Dramatists Play Service for more information about using it in your production. There may be fees associated with the use of this song in performance.

Beethoven's "Moonlight Sonata" is required for production. The song itself is in the public domain, but it is the reponsibility of the producing theater/organization to secure permission to use any recording of the song that is copyrighted.

Dramatists Play Service neither holds the rights to nor grants permission to use any other songs or recordings mentioned in the Play. It is the responsibility of the producing theater/organization to obtain permission of the copyright owner(s) for any such use. Additional royalty fees may apply for the right to use copyrighted materials.

For any other songs/recordings, images, or design elements mentioned in the play, works in the public domain may be substituted. It is the producing theater/organization's responsibility to ensure the substituted work is indeed in the public domain. Dramatists Play Service, Inc., cannot advise as to whether or not a song/arrangement/recording, image, or other design element is in the public domain.